CLAMP

TRANSLATED AND ADAPTED BY
Anthony Gerard

LETTERED BY
Dana Hayward

LONDON

Published in the United Kingdom by Tanoshimi in 2006

5 7 9 10 8 6 4

Tsubasa copyright © CLAMP, 2004
English translation copyright © CLAMP, 2005

First published in Japan in 2003 by Kodansha Ltd., Tokyo

Published by arrangement with Kodansha Ltd., Tokyo and with Del Rey,
an imprint of Random House Inc., New York

Tanoshimi
Random House, 20 Vauxhall Bridge Road,
London, SW1V 2SA

www.tanoshimi.tv
www.rbooks.co.uk

Addresses for companies within The Random House Group Limited can be found at:
www.randomhouse.co.uk

Random House Group Limited Reg. No. 954009

A CIP catalogue record for this book is available from the British Library

ISBN 9780099504122

The Random House Group Limited supports The Forest Stewardship Council (FSC), the leading
international forest certification organisation. All our titles that are printed on Greenpeace
approved FSC certified paper carry the FSC logo. Our paper procurement policy can be found at:
www.rbooks.co.uk/environment

Printed and bound in Germany by GGP Media GmbH, Pößneck

Translated and adapted by Anthony Gerrad
Lettered by Dana Hayward

Tsubasa Volume I crosses over with *xxxHOLiC* Volume I. Although it isn't necessary to read *xxxHOLiC* to understand the events in *Tsubasa*, you'll get to see the same events from different perspectives if you read both!

Contents

Honorifics

Throughout the Tanoshimi Manga books, you will find Japanese honorifics left intact in the translations. For those not familiar with how the Japanese use honorifics, and more importantly, how they differ from English honorifics, we present this brief overview.

Politeness has always been a critical facet of Japanese culture. Ever since the feudal era, when Japan was a highly stratified society, use of honorifics—which can be defined as polite speech that indicates relationship or status—has played an essential role in the Japanese language. When addressing someone in Japanese, an honorific usually takes the form of a suffix attached to one's name (example: "Asuna-san"), or as a title at the end of one's name or in place of the name itself (example: "Negi-sensei," or simply "Sensei!").

Honorifics can be expressions of respect or endearment. In the context of manga and anime, honorifics give insight into the nature of the relationship between characters. Many translations into English leave out these important honorifics, and therefore distort the "feel" of the original Japanese. Because Japanese honorifics contain nuances that English honorifics lack, it is our policy at Tanoshimi not to translate them. Here, instead, is a guide to some of the honorifics you may encounter in Tanoshimi Manga.

-san: This is the most common honorific, and is equivalent to Mr., Miss, Ms., Mrs., etc. It is the all-purpose honorific and can be used in any situation where politeness is required.

-sama: This is one level higher than "-san." It is used to confer great respect.

-dono: This comes from the word "tono," which means "lord." It is even a higher level than "-sama," and confers utmost respect.

-kun: This suffix is used at the end of boys' names to express familiarity or endearment. It is also sometimes used by men among friends, or when addressing someone younger or of a lower station.

-chan: This is used to express endearment, mostly toward girls. It is also used for little boys, pets, and even among lovers. It gives a sense of childish cuteness.

Sempai: This title suggests that the addressee is one's "senior" in a group or organization. It is most often used in a school setting, where underclassmen refer to their upperclassmen as "sempai." It can also be used in the workplace, such as when a newer employee addresses an employee who has seniority in the company.

Kohai: This is the opposite of "-sempai," and is used toward underclassmen in school or newcomers in the workplace. It connotes that the addressee is of lower station.

Sensei: Literally meaning "one who has come before," this title is used for teachers, doctors, or masters of any profession or art.

[blank]: Usually forgotten in these lists, but perhaps the most significant difference between Japanese and English. The lack of honorific means that the speaker has permission to address the person in a very intimate way. Usually, only family, spouses, or very close friends have this kind of permission. Known as *yobisute*, it can be gratifying when someone who has earned the intimacy starts to call one by one's name without an honorific. But when that intimacy hasn't been earned, it can also be very insulting.

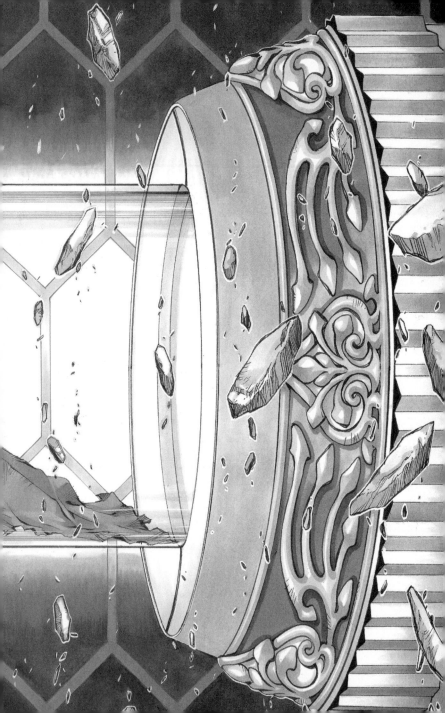

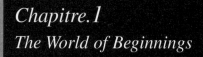

Chapitre.1
The World of Beginnings

RESERVoir CHRoNiCLE

TSUBASA

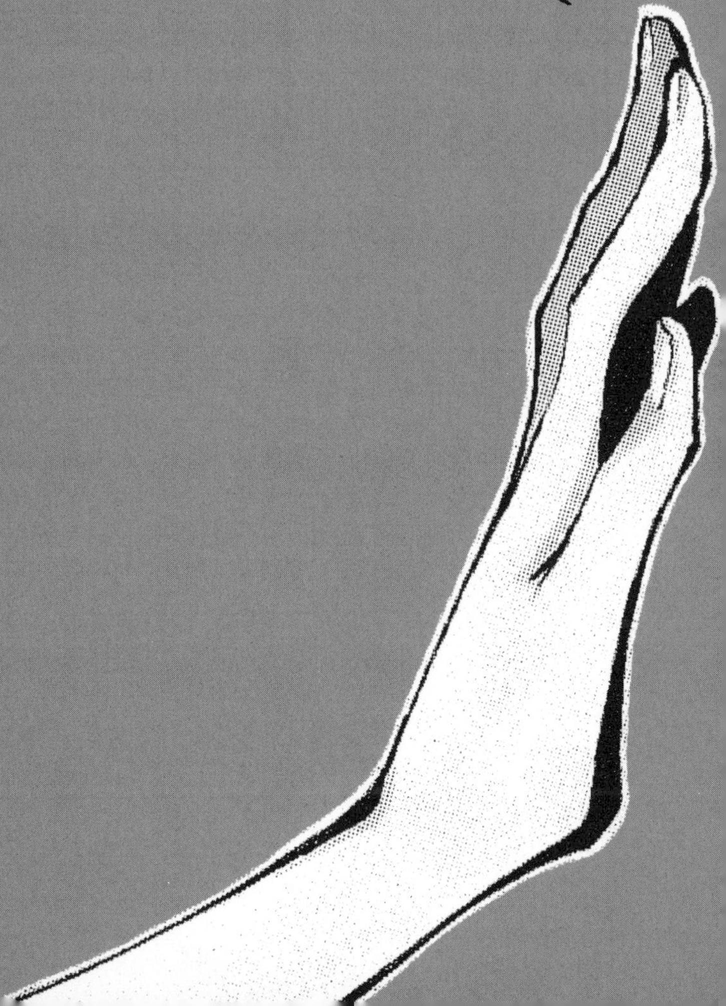

HELLO, FATHER ...

... I'M HOME.

JUST LIKE YOU THEORIZED, FATHER.

YOU WERE RIGHT. IN THIS COUNTRY THE RUINS YOU SEE ARE ONLY THE TIP OF LARGER STRUCTURES BURIED IN THE SAND.

THE UNEARTHING OF THE EASTERN RUINS IS WELL UNDERWAY.

BAM BAM

YES?

KA-CHAK

14

SWIP

"SAKURA"!

HEH
HEH
HEH

S—

S—
SAKURA.

NICE TO BE BACK.

ほの
WHSPR

ぼの
WHSPR

SYAORAN.

I'M REALLY HAPPY THAT YOU'RE HOME.

CHIPOK

ちょこん
...

GASP!

OH, I'M SORRY! I'M CUTTING OFF THE BLOOD TO YOUR LEGS!

...WHEN I WOULD BE COMING BACK.

SAKURA, YOU KNEW...

YOUR HIGH-NESS KNEW—

HE TOLD US THAT THERE ARE PROBABLY RUINS BURIED BENEATH THE SANDS OF THE DESERT.

HE EXPLAINED TO THE PREVIOUS KING, MY FATHER, HOW WE COULD UNDERSTAND OUR COUNTRY'S HISTORY IF HE COULD BE ALLOWED TO EXCAVATE.

THE DESERT IS ALWAYS DANGEROUS, SO THE EXCAVATION TOOK CAREFUL PLANNING.

AND WHEN THE PREPARATIONS WERE FINALLY COMPLETE, THE DIGGING BEGAN.

HE DIED DURING THE DIG...

...BUT HIS LIFE WAS A HAPPY ONE.

HE WAS SMILING UNTIL THE LAST.

BESIDES, I CAN AFFORD TO LIVE ON MY OWN WITH THE MONEY FROM THE DIG.

BUT...

GRMP

WE INVITED YOU TO COME LIVE WITH US WHEN HE PASSED AWAY!

WHY DIDN'T YOU?

YOU'RE ROYALTY! I'M A COMMONER! COMMONERS CAN'T LIVE IN THE CASTLE!

IT'S NOT WEIRD! AFTER ALL, WE'VE BEEN FRIENDS SINCE WE WERE KIDS!

I WOULD HAVE FELT WEIRD LIVING IN A CASTLE.

I *DO* THINK OF YOU!
AND I WONDER, 'WHAT'S SAKURA DOING NOW?'
UM... YOU KNOW, I...
I MEAN...
THERE'S SOME-THING I...
...WANTED TO...
...TELL...
...YOU.
? WHAT IS IT?

THANKS!

THIS IS THE MOST PEACEFUL COUNTRY WE'VE EVER BEEN TO.

MY FATHER AND I TRAVELED TO ALL SORTS OF DIFFERENT COUNTRIES.

THAT REALLY IS TRUE.

THAT THING I WANTED TO TELL YOU?

WHEN WE MEET NEXT, I'LL TELL YOU THEN.

UM...

YOU KNOW...

OH. OKAY.

...SO WAIT A BIT.

OKAY?

I *WILL* TELL YOU...

26

27

HE LISTENED TO THEIR ENTIRE REPORT.

RIGHT THERE ON HIS THRONE

THEN TÔYA GOT SELFISH AND SKIPPED OUT, RIGHT?

NO, I'M NOT *YOU!*

WHAT DID YOU SAY?!

AND SOON THEY'LL FINISH DIGGING THE WHOLE THING *UP!*

IT SEEMS SO, YOUR HIGH-NESS.

THEY'VE COME A LONG WAY ON THE DIG.

IT LOOKS LIKE THERE IS MORE TO THESE RUINS THAN WHAT IS ABOVE GROUND.

NO.

AND THE TWERP WILL BE BUSY FOR A

THE EXCAVATION WILL GO ON.

LONG

LONG

LONG

LONG

TIME TO COME.

THEY'VE DISCOVERED A NEW UNDER-GROUND PATH.

WHAT?!

I DON'T KNOW HOW FAR IT'S GOING TO TAKE THEM, BUT I'VE GIVEN PERMISSION TO CONTINUE DIGGING.

AND SO...

AND IF THERE'S SOME NEW RUIN, I'M SURE THAT'LL MAKE HIM THE HAPPIEST MAN ALIVE! SO IT'S *FINE WITH ME!!*

SYAORAN'S JUST LIKE HIS FATHER! HE LOVES RUINS AND HISTORY AND STUFF LIKE THAT!

TH-THAT'S JUST FINE WITH ME!

30

YUKITO. I TOLD YOU THAT WHEN WE'RE ALONE, YOU CAN DROP THE FORMALITIES.

BUT...

STOMP STOMP

...PROVOKE HER SO, YOUR MAJESTY. YOU SHOULD NOT...

...BUT WHEN THE JOB IS OVER, WE'RE JUST OLD FRIENDS.

TO THE PUBLIC WE MAY BE KING AND HIGH PRIEST...

HE JUST GETS ON MY NERVES. THE LITTLE TWERP.

OKAY. AH! YES, YOUR M—

SHA POK

...IT *REALLY* GETS ON MY NERVES!

HOWEVER...

YOUR PREDICTIONS OF THE FUTURE ARE NEVER WRONG.

AND THAT'S WHY...

...THE TWO OF THEM HAVE ADVERSITY WAITING AHEAD.

THE PRINCESS HAS AN UNUSUAL POWER.

I CAN'T SAY THAT I UNDERSTAND IT MYSELF.

ADVERSITY LIKE YOU'VE NEVER SEEN.

BUT I *CAN* SAY...

34

36

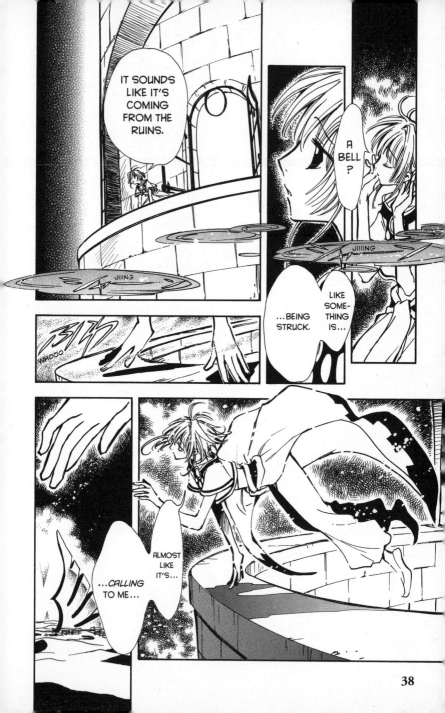

38

GASP

WAS
THAT...

SYAORAN
?

WHAT...

WHAT
WAS
THAT?

AND THAT WHICH POINTS THE WAY ARE THE WINGS...

...THE "TSUBASA"!

THE POWER TO PASS THROUGH SPACE AND TIME.

AND NOW ...

...THAT POWER IS REBORN!

57

THE WINGS AND THE PRINCESS'S HEART ARE ONE.

HER... HEART?

HOW CAN THAT—

...HER HEART IS NOWHERE TO BE FOUND ON THIS WORLD!

AND...

ALL OF THE PRINCESS'S MEMORIES FROM THE MOMENT OF HER BIRTH TO NOW HAVE VANISHED.

WHO IS THAT PERSON? WHAT SHOULD I DO WHEN WE MEET?

SHE IS CALLED THE *TIME-SPACE WITCH!*

YOU WILL TELL HER EVERY-THING, AND...

SAKURA!!

ARE YOU...

ARE YOU THE SPACE-TIME WITCH?

I HAVE BEEN CALLED THAT.

64

RESERVoir CHRoNiCLE

Chapitre.2
The Price of Memory

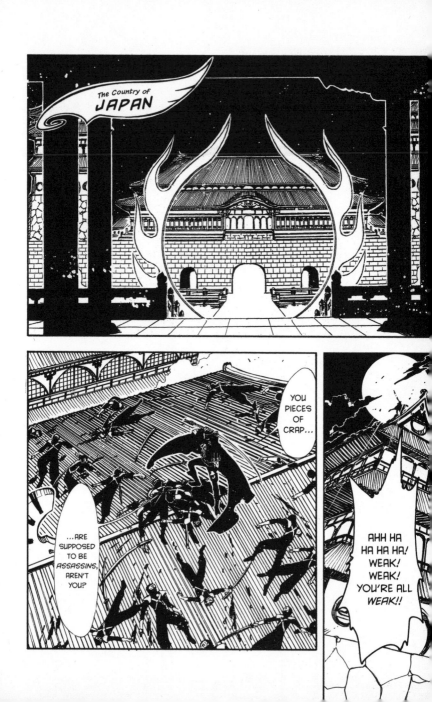

ONE OF THE FIRST RULES FOR NINJA IS TO CUT DOWN THOSE WHO ATTACK YOU, PRINCESS TOMOYO.

I ASKED YOU TO AVOID UNNECESSARY DEATH...

...WEREN'T THOSE MY WORDS?

AAAAAH!

I HAVE NEVER HEARD SUCH A RULE.

CAN'T YOU JUST SHUT UP?

GUESS THERE HAVE TO BE GOOD ONES AND BAD ONES.

HEH!

WITH SUCH LOYAL, GOOD NINJA AS SÔMA, WHY ARE THERE ALSO SUCH NINJA AS YOU, KUROGANE?

NO, DON'T BOTHER, SÔMA.

KUROGANE! HOW CAN YOU BE SO RUDE TO HER HIGHNESS?!

70

73

74

The Country of
SERESU

76

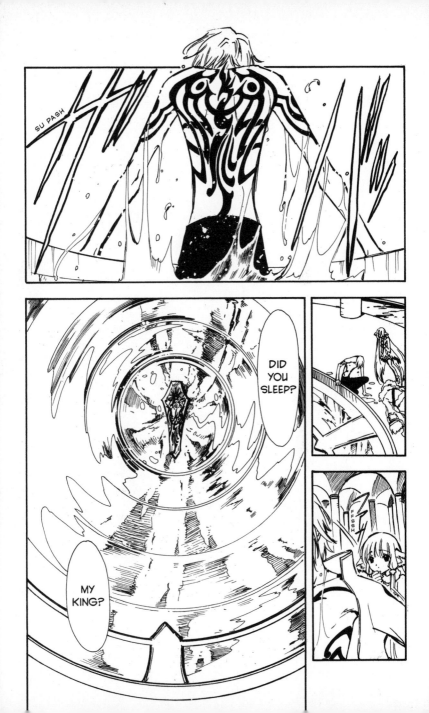

YES.

THIS IS THE ONLY WAY I CAN.

WHAT WILL YOU DO NOW...

...FAI?

I CAN'T STAY IN THIS COUNTRY ANY LONGER.

SO I WONDER IF IT'S ALL RIGHT TO CHANGE YOU A LITTLE.

PAAA AAA

IT'S JUST FINE.

I WANT YOU TO TELL ME IF THE KING AWAKENS.

BUT I HAVE A FAVOR TO ASK OF YOU, CHI.

WHAT IS IT?

AFTER ALL, FAI *MADE* CHI!

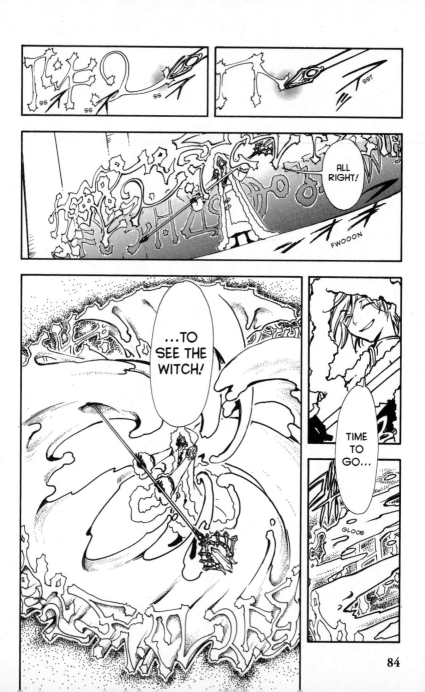

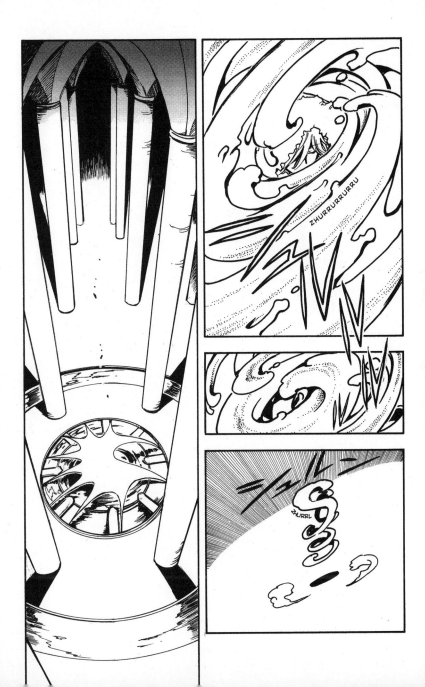

YES!

I'M SYAORAN.

AND YOU?

THIS CHILD'S NAME IS SAKURA, ISN'T IT?

...YES.

...HAS LOST SOMETHING VERY PRECIOUS.

THIS CHILD...

92

THE WIZARD OF SERESU.

FAI D. FLOWRIGHT.

SHT

DO YOU KNOW WHERE YOU ARE?

AND SO...

...THE REASON WHY ALL OF YOU ARE HERE...

...IS BECAUSE EACH OF YOU HAS A WISH.

THAT'S EXACTLY IT.

YES...

A PLACE WHERE ANY WISH CAN BE GRANTED IF A SUITABLE PRICE IS PAID.

STARE

MY HOME WORLD...

...IS THE PLACE I DO *NOT* WANT TO BE.

...IS WHERE I WANT TO BE!

THAT IS A TALL ORDER...

...FOR BOTH OF YOU.

NO...

...FOR ALL *THREE* OF YOU...

... PERHAPS.

WHAT KIND OF *CRAP* ARE YOU SPOUTING?

MR. BLACK, CAN YOU KEEP YOUR INSULTS DOWN?

HEY!

I'M KUROGANE!!

I'M *NOT* "MR. BLACK!"

...BUT...

...IF ALL THREE PAID TOGETHER, YOU MAY JUST BE ABLE TO AFFORD IT.

EVEN IF YOU OFFERED THE MOST PRECIOUS THINGS YOU OWN, NONE OF YOU HAS ENOUGH TO PAY...

ALL THREE OF YOUR WISHES ARE THE SAME.

96

97

HUH ?

POLEE ?

TIIVII ?

ZMM

INSTEAD YOU WILL WANDER THIS WORLD LOOKING LIKE A COSTUME-CONTEST LOSER, AND GET PICKED UP BY THE POLICE FOR CARRYING AN UNLAWFUL SWORD, AND GET PLASTERED ALL OVER THE TV FOR BEING A FREAK! IS THAT WHAT YOU WANT?

FINE!

ZMM

TWIK

ZMM

THAT'S GOT TO BE A LIE!!

YOU REALIZE THAT YOU ARE TRAPPED HERE, AND I AM THE ONLY PERSON IN THE WORLD WHO CAN GET YOU OUT?

IT'S ALL TRUE.

EH HEH HEH

YOU'RE KIDDING!

WHAT WILL YOU DO?

100

THERE IS "HITSUZEN."

WHAT *IS*

HOWEVER, THERE IS NO COINCIDENCE IN THE WORLD.

AND WHAT BROUGHT YOU TOGETHER...

...WAS ALSO "HITSUZEN."

SYAORAN...

...YOUR PRICE IS...

...YOUR RELATION- SHIP.

106

107

Chapitre.3
The Wings of Hitsuzen

114

MOKONA DRIED TOO!

WE TRIED TO DRY HER OFF.

SHE GOT PRETTY WET IN THE RAIN.

PRAISE ME!

SEEP SEEP

SO YOU...

EVEN WHILE YOU SLEPT, YOU WOULDN'T LET THE GIRL GO.

CALL ME SYAORAN.

ER...

AND SO...

...MY GUESS IS WITHOUT THINKING, YOU GRABBED IT YOURSELF.

THAT'S ...

...WHAT THE WITCH SAID, WASN'T IT?

BYUUN

IN ORDER TO SAVE THE GIRL.

I DOUBT WE'LL FIND ANY MORE IN OUR CLOTHES.

BUT MY QUESTION IS HOW CAN WE FIND THEM NOW...

MUDGE MUDGE

...NEW FEATHERS.

OF COURSE, I'M JUST GUESSING ALL THIS!

SLUMP

.....

EH?

126

133

134

RESERVoir CHRoNiCLE

Chapitre.4
The Strength to Fight

140

DOES EVERYONE IN THIS COUNTRY HAVE AN ACCENT LIKE YOURS, SORATA-SAN?

A BASEBALL? WHAT THE HELL IS THAT?

YES?

FAI-KUN?

YOURS IS A LANGUAGE THAT THEY USED IN THE PAST?

MY ACCENT IS UNIQUE TO ME. IT'S AN OLDER VERSION OF OUR LANGUAGE.

OKAAAY!

OKAAAY!

SORA-CHAN?

.....

AWW, DON'T BE SO FORMAL! CALL ME SORA-CHAN!

YOU'RE A HISTORY TEACHER?

BOING

I'M A HISTORY TEACHER, AND I'M FIRMLY AGAINST ALLOWING ALL THE OLD WAYS TO FADE AWAY.

THAT'S RIGHT!

NOWADAYS HARDLY ANYONE USES THIS LANGUAGE.

143

144

"KUDAN"?

YOU ALL COME FROM DIFFERENT WORLDS! YOU *WOULDN'T* KNOW!

SURE YOU DON'T!

YOU DON'T KNOW?

WHILE YOU'RE ON THIS WORLD, I'LL VOUCH FOR YOU.

FINE.

THANK YOU...

...MOKONA!

YOU CAN USE THESE ROOMS UNTIL YOU GO TO YOUR NEXT WORLD.

THIS IS AN APARTMENT BUILDING. WE'VE GOT ROOM.

THANK YOU VERY MUCH!

I OWE YÛKO-SAN A FAVOR.

155

157

Chapitre.5
The Instant of Awakening

MOKONA ISN'T A WHITE THING! MOKONA IS MOKONA!

BAA

STAY AWAY!

IS THE WHITE THING COMING ALONG, TOO?

I'LL STAY BY SAKURA-SAN'S SIDE FOR YOU.

THANK YOU.

DUCK

HUH?

WHAT I MEAN IS THIS WORLD IS USED TO WEIRD SIGHTS.

GRRRR

RIGHT!

IF MOKONA IS A WHITE THING, THEN THIS GUY HERE IS A BLACK THING, RIGHT?

YOU HAVE TO TAKE MOKONA, OR YOU'LL PASS THE FEATHER BY AND NEVER KNOW!

DON'T WORRY. NOBODY WILL GIVE MOKONA A SECOND THOUGHT.

NOW...

THERE'S ENOUGH FOR LUNCH IN THERE, SO THE THREE OF YOU SHOULD TAKE YOUR TIME AND MAKE FRIENDS.

WELL, YOU CAN EAT WHERE YOU LIKE, BUT YOU'LL NEVER FIND A BETTER MEAL THAN MY HONEY MAKES!

TAKE THIS.

WHY'S HE GIVING IT TO THE *KID*?!

WHAT'S *THAT* SUPPOSED TO MEAN?

CAUSE HE'S THE ONE WHO LOOKS THE MOST TRUSTWORTHY!

167

168

169

IT WOULD TAKE GOING TO A LOT OF WORLDS TO BE ABLE TO COLLECT ALL OF SAKURA-CHAN'S FEATHERS.

AND I THINK THE ONLY ONE WHO CAN SEND SOMEONE TO MANY WORLDS IS THE DIMENSION WITCH.

"YOUR HIGHNESS, WOULD YOU HAVE AN APPLE?"

"THANK YOU!"

177

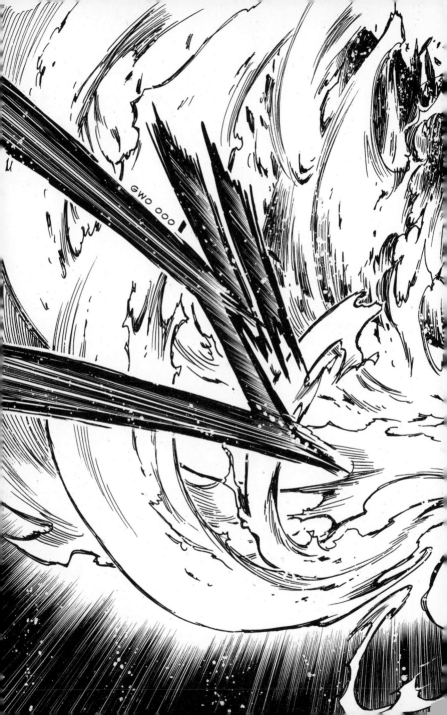

To Be Continued

About the Creators

CLAMP is a group of four women who have become the most popular manga artists in The United Kingdom—Ageha Ohkawa, Mokona, Satsuki Igarashi, and Tsubaki Nekoi. They started out as doujnishi (fan comics) creators, but their skill and craft brought them to the attention of publishers very quickly. Their first work from a major publisher was *RG Veda*, but their first mass success was with *Magic Knight Rayearth*. From there, they went on to write many series, including *Cardcaptor Sakura* and *Chobits* Volumes 1, 2 & 3 of *xxxHOLiC* and *Tsubasa* are available from Tanoshimi now. Like many Japanese manga artists, they prefer to avoid the spotlight, and little is known about them personally.

CLAMP is currently publishing three series in Japan: *Tsubasa* and *xxxHOLiC* with Kodansha and *Gohou Drug* with Kadokawa.

Past Works

CLAMP has created many series. Here is a brief overview of one of them.

Cardcaptor Sakura

The first volume of *Cardcaptor Sakura* was released in Japan in 1996, and by the time the series was finished it would number twelve volumes in all. The first six, called simply *Cardcaptor Sakura*, are the story of fourth-grader Sakura, who finds a magic book called *The Clow* in her father's library. The book and its magical guardian, Kero, were responsible for containing the Clow Cards. The Clow Cards, created by sorcerer Clow Reed, have escaped, and Kero needs Sakura's help to find them. Empowered with the key to recapture them, Sakura becomes a Cardcaptor and begins her quest for all of the lost Clow cards.

Over the course of the next six volumes, we are introduced to a wide range of characters, some of whom will be familiar to you after you've read the first volume of *Tsubasa*. Toya is Sakura's brother, and Yukito is his best friend. Li Syaoran is Sakura's erstwhile competitor in capturing the Clow Cards. Still, there are more characters that don't appear in *Tsubasa* than do, such as Kero, the guardian.

If you've read *Cardcaptor Sakura*, even the characters you recognize will seem radically different. The *Tsubasa* versions of Sakura and Syaoran both seem to be teenagers, several years older than their counterparts. Toya is a king, while Yuki is his chief advisor. Toya and Sakura's parents aren't in the picture, while Tomoyo lives in yet another dimension and appears to have no knowledge of Sakura whatsoever!

Cardcaptor Sakura was released in anime form in two versions in the United States. Pioneer released the Japanese version on DVD, while Nelvana released a reworked version on television called simply *Cardcaptors*. *Cardcaptors* was short-lived and incurred the ire of many fans because it was heavily edited and reworked to make it more palatable for an Western audience.

In the manga, the main storyline ends in volume six when Sakura successfully captures all of the Clow Cards and is named Master of the Clow. It almost looks like it's time for Sakura to hang up her wand for good, but CLAMP still had a few more stories in mind—and another six volumes to go!

Dramatis Personae

You'd need a scorecard to keep track of all the characters who will be appearing in *Tsubasa* and *xxxHOLiC*, so we've decided to create one for you. Some of these characters will look familiar, but you haven't really met most of them before. Don't read these if you haven't read this volume yet—there's a reason we put them at the end of the book!

Sakura

While it's clear that Sakura is older than her counterpart from *Cardcaptor Sakura*, we don't actually know her age yet. She is the princess of Clow, raised by her brother, King Toya. She's a happy princess, well-loved by her people. Sakura possesses the power to change the world, but it will be a while before she—or we—understand what that means.

Syaoran

Syaoran's father died in an archaeological dig, leaving him an orphan, but Syaoran felt compelled to continue his father's work. He's closer than ever to uncovering the secrets of the giant wings buried in the sand, but a threat to Sakura's safety sends him on a quest to save her life! The *Tsubasa* version of Syaoran is very different from the character in *Cardcaptor Sakura*. Where the *CS* Syaoran is dour, surly, even rude at times, *Tsubasa*'s version is open, friendly—and clearly in love with Sakura.

Tomoyo

In *CS*, Tomoyo was Sakura's best friend who videotaped her card-capturing exploits. In *Tsubasa*, Tomoyo is the queen of another realm, and like Yukito, she is a powerful sorceress. It remains to be seen if her role in this drama is concluded.

Fai D. Florite

Fai's motivation for visiting Yûko, the space-time witch, isn't entirely clear. Like Tomoyo, he is the ruler of his land of Seresu. He may be fleeing a battle he's lost, or he may desperately need to get away from a battle he's won—we just don't know yet. What we do know is that he is the creator of this world's version of Chi, a character from CLAMP's *Chobits*, and that he is fleeing from Ashura, a variation of the main character of CLAMP's first series, *RG Veda*.

Chi

In *Chobits*, Chi was a persocom, a personal computer found by Hideki Motosuwa. With her memory wiped clean, Chi and Hideki have a lot of work to do to discover her origins. Along the way, each discovers a lot more about themselves and about their feelings for each other. Of course, that's assuming that a machine can even have feelings in the first place. . . .

The *Tsubasa* version of Chi was created by Fai, so she is clearly *not* the same character as in *Chobits*, although her personality appears remarkably similar. As Fai begins his quest, he leaves Chi behind to guard against King Ashura's awakening.

Yûko

Yûko is a witch. She lives in a peculiar house in Tokyo with two peculiar helpers, Maru and Moru. Her work is simple: She helps people . . . for a price. The price is never more than her customer can bear, but the greater the need, the higher it gets. Yûko is something of an enigma: She comes across as very mysterious and all-knowing, but she also has a playful, sometimes wild side that leads to unfortunate side effects. Like hangovers.

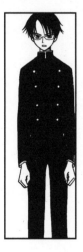

Watanuki

Watanuki Kimihiro will pop up in *Tsubasa* from time to time, but his home is over in *xxxHOLiC*, where he works for Yûko, cleaning, cooking, gardening, and doing whatever other chores Yûko can come up with. It's the price he pays for Yûko to grant his wish—to be rid of the spirit visions that haunt him. Although he's a hard worker, he often finds working for Yûko to be a frustrating experience.

Sorata (Sora) Arisugawa

When Sora was three years old, the Buddhist monks of Mt. Koya recognized Sora as a future Dragon of Heaven. Knowing that he would develop powers that could help to save the earth, the monks started training him, and Sora's irrepressible personality turned the monastery upside down. But when the three-year-old Sora was parted from his mother, the tears in her eyes affected him deeply. He determined that he would find the one girl for him, and he would protect her. He would protect her and die for her so that she may never feel hurt the way his mother did. In the story of X (*X/1999*), the girl he found was Arashi Kishu.

Arashi Kishu

At age six, Arashi was wandering the streets eating out of garbage cans and wondering if life was really worth it. Her mother had died three months earlier, and although she had asked Arashi to somehow survive, Arashi was beginning to have second thoughts. Being found by her mother's old Shinto teacher and brought into a beautiful shrine still didn't answer Arashi's question of whether to die or go on living. The promise of becoming a Dragon of Heaven, and more importantly, having friends in the future so that she wouldn't be alone, made Arashi decide to give life a try. In the story of X (*X/1999*), she grew into a Shinto "miko" priestess and joined the Seven Seals.

Translation Notes

Japanese is a tricky language for most westerners, and translation is often more art than science. For your edification and reading pleasure, here are notes on some of the places where we could have gone in a different direction in our translation of the work, or where a Japanese cultural reference is used.

The Kingdom of Clow

Made up of the characters Eternal and Tower, the pronunciation *kurô* sounds suspiciously like Clow.

Intimacy

After Sakura and Syaoran's conversation, you should notice a distinct similarity between that conversation and the later one of Tôya and Yukito.

It's all about intimacy. Once two people are close enough friends, they drop the honorifics and titles (see *Honorifics* at the front of the book) and the grammar of polite language, and they become more direct and easygoing.

Ginryû

The characters for Ginryû mean "silver dragon," which gives you the reason for the dragon on the hilt.

Hitsuzen

This is actually defined by Yûko in *xxxHOLiC* Volume 1: "Hitsuzen. A naturally foreordained event. A state in which other outcomes are impossible. A result which can only be obtained by a single causality, and other causalities would necessarily create different results."

Kuro-chan, Kuro-rin . . .

All of the names that Fai is trying to give Kurogane are the type of nicknames that one would give cute high-school girls (ko-gals), or that cute high-school girls would give themselves.

Sora's Accent

Accents in Japanese and English work somewhat differently. In English, an accent is mostly marked by pronunciation—especially of the vowel sounds—and a few differences in vocabulary. So if you take a little time to get used to the differences, you will have no problem understanding even the thickest accent in English. In Japanese, there are some pronunciation differences, but most of the differences are in vocabulary. Since the differences start at the core vocabulary (even the ubiquitous verb "to be"!), and spread throughout, a thick accent is nearly as difficult to understand as a completely different language. Fortunately for most Japanese citizens, the Osaka dialect is very popular in the media, so everyone is used to the different words, even if they didn't grow up in the Osaka area.

The Hanshin Republic

For those who don't know Japanese baseball, the most popular team in Japan is the Yomiuri Giants. The second most popular team is the Hanshin Tigers, and like other second-mosts, the fans of the Hanshin Tigers are fiercely competitive and fanatical. None more than Sora's character, and so, the Hanshin Republic is the fondest dream of Tigers' fans—an entire nation devoted body and soul to Osaka's favorite baseball club. More on this in Volume 2!

The logo for the Hanshin Tigers

197

Preview of *Tsubasa* Volume 2

Here is an excerpt from Volume 2, on sale now in English.